STICKER BOOK

KINGS
AND
QUEENS
of England

Written by Rosy Border
Illustrated by Bob Moulder

HENDERSON
PUBLISHING PLC

©1995 HENDERSON PUBLISHING PLC

INTRODUCTION

Until quite recently, all English schoolchildren had to learn the names of the Kings and Queens of England. There were several rhymes to help them remember. Here is just one of those rhymes:

**Billy, Billy, Henry, Steve,
Henry, Dick, John, Henry Three.
Three Teds, then Richard Two;
Three more Henries - then what's new?
Two more Teds, then Dick the Bad,
Two more Henries, Ted the Lad.
Mary, Bess and Scottish Jim,
Charles - but they beheaded him!
One more Charles, then Jamie Two;
Bill-and-Mary, Anne - then who?
Four Georges, Billy, then Victoria -
These lists of names were sent to bore ya!
Ted the Seventh liked his fun,
Georgie was the quiet one.
Ted came when Mrs Simpson beckoned,
Then came George and Bess the Second.**

In other words: William I, William II, Henry I, Stephen, Henry II, Richard I, John, Henry III, Edwards I, II and III, Richard II, Henries IV, V, VI, Edward IV, Edward V, Richard III, Henry VII, Henry VIII, Edward VI, Mary, Elizabeth I, James I, Charles I, Charles II, James II, William III and Mary, Anne, Georges I, II, III, IV, William IV, Victoria, Edward VII, George V, Edward VIII, George VI, Elizabeth II.

If you find this list easier to remember or more interesting than the rhyme, good luck to you...

WILLIAM I (HOUSE OF NORMANDY)

> • 1027 - 1087 • crowned age 39 • king for 21 years • married Matilda of Flanders • 4 children

The English king, Edward the Confessor, had no children. William Duke of Normandy, Edward's cousin, claimed the King had promised him the throne. Harold of England said the throne belonged to him. William invaded England with 700 ships and his army fought Harold's at Hastings. Harold was killed and William was crowned King of England on Christmas Day 1066.

Strip Cartoon

The Bayeux Tapestry tells the story of William's invasion of England. It is like a strip cartoon, except that the captions are in Latin.

William took land away from Englishmen and gave it to his own men, the barons. The King gave them lands and castles, and in return the barons had to supply the King with money and soldiers.

To find out what taxes his new subjects should pay, William ordered the Domesday Book, a list of all the property in the country.

WILLIAM II (HOUSE OF NORMANDY)

> • 1056 - 1100 • crowned age 31 • king for
> 13 years • never married • no children

William I had three sons, Robert, William and Henry,
and a daughter, Adela. (Remember Adela; her son,
Stephen, later became King of England). Robert,
the eldest son, became Duke of Normandy and
William, who was called Rufus because of his red
face, became King of England. (What happened
to Henry? See Page 5).

Robert wanted to go on a crusade (more about
crusades later). To equip his army, he pawned
Normandy to William. If he did not repay the
money, Normandy would belong to William.

Who Shot the King?

In 1100, Robert was on his way home with a rich
wife to buy back Normandy. But before Robert
returned, William was shot while hunting. Was it an
accident or an assassination? His brother, Henry,
was nearby that day, but nobody knows what
really happened.

HENRY I (HOUSE OF NORMANDY)

> • 1068 - 1135 • crowned age 32
> • king for 35 years • married: **1** Matilda
> of Scotland **2** Adela of Louvain • 2 children

As soon as William Rufus died, Henry had himself crowned king.

When Robert came home, he and Henry argued. Henry defeated Robert in battle and took him prisoner. Now Henry was both King of England and Duke of Normandy.

Henry's only son died in a shipwreck. Henry married again, but he did not have any more children. So Henry's daughter, Matilda, wife of Emperor Henry V of Germany, was next in line to the throne. When the Emperor died, Henry married Matilda to Robert's grandson, 14 year old Geoffrey Plantagenet. Princesses did not marry for love in those days. They went where they were sent.

A Surfeit of Lampreys

Henry died of a surfeit of lampreys. A surfeit is too much of a good thing and lampreys are fish. You could say that too many fish caused a war - see Stephen, next in line.

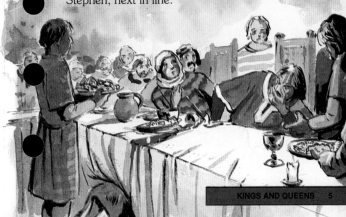

STEPHEN (HOUSE OF NORMANDY)

> • 1097 - 1154 • crowned age 38 • king for
> 19 years • married Matilda of Boulogne • 1 child

Stephen told everyone that Henry I had changed his mind on his deathbed and picked him to be king. This was a lie, but Stephen was crowned in Westminster Abbey.

Civil War

Matilda and Geoffrey came back to claim their rights, and there was war. First Matilda captured Stephen. The next year Matilda herself was taken prisoner, but she escaped through the snow, wrapped in a white cloak.

The war dragged on until Matilda had lost heart. Her son, Henry, ruled the Norman lands. Then in 1152, the French king divorced his wife, Eleanor of Aquitaine, and Henry immediately married her. This gave him Aquitaine, another big slice of France.

The fighting went on and on. Then Stephen's only son, Eustace, died. It was agreed that Stephen should be king for life, and that Matilda's son, Henry, should rule after him as Henry II.

HENRY II (HOUSE OF PLANTAGENET)

> • 1133 - 89 • crowned age 21 • king for 35 years
> • married Eleanor of Aquitaine • 7 children

Henry inherited England and a huge chunk of France. Even the Scottish, Irish and Welsh kings had to be polite to him. He was a good king, but is remembered as the man who encouraged his men to murder Thomas Becket, the Archbishop of Canterbury, in Canterbury Cathedral.

Murder in the Cathedral

Becket started off as Henry's friend and chief minister. Henry wanted to make the Church less powerful and thought that by making his friend the Archbishop of Canterbury - the top priest in the land - he would get his own way. He was wrong. Becket took the Church's side. In a fury, Henry shouted, "Will no one rid me of this turbulent priest?" Some of his knights heard him and murdered Becket.

The Church quickly made Becket a saint and Canterbury became a holy place. Chaucer's Canterbury Tales are stories told by pilgrims on their way there.

RICHARD I (HOUSE OF PLANTAGENET)

> • 1157 - 1199 • crowned age 32 • king for 10 years
> • married Berengaria of Navarre • no children

Richard's nickname was Coeur de Lion - Lionheart - for his bravery in battle. He fought in the Crusades, a holy war to control places such as Jerusalem, which were important to Christians.

He was taken prisoner on his way home and his enemies demanded an enormous ransom. His brother, Prince John, wanted to be king and tried his utmost to prevent Richard's release, but Richard's loyal subjects raised the money. They did not see much of their king, however. Soon he was off to war again, and was killed in battle in France - so bad Prince John became king anyway.

JOHN (HOUSE OF PLANTAGENET)

> • 1167 - 1216 • crowned age 32 • king for 17 years
> • married: **1** Alice **2** Avisa **3** Isabella • 2 children

John's nickname was "Lackland" because he lost so much of the land in France that he had inherited. He quarrelled with the Church, the French king (which is how he lost his land) and his own barons.

The Magna Carta

In 1215, the barons forced John to sign a document called the Magna Carta, which means the Great Charter, which limited the King's powers and laid down the law of the land.

HENRY III (HOUSE OF PLANTAGENET)

> • 1207 - 1272 • crowned age 9 • king for 56 years
> • married Eleanor of Provence • 2 children

Henry was not a very well-liked king. He annoyed his barons so much that they took over the kingdom themselves. Their leader, Simon de Montfort, the King's brother-in-law, founded a Great Council, which was an early form of today's Parliament. For a year the Great Council ruled the kingdom. When Henry got his crown back he behaved more sensibly.

At the time of his death, the country was more united and much more prosperous. He is remembered, though, as "the simple king".

EDWARD I (HOUSE OF PLANTAGENET)

> • 1239 - 1307 • crowned age 33
> • king for 35 years • married: **1** Eleanor of Castille
> **2** Margaret of France • 1 child

Edward was a great fighter. He killed Simon de Montfort and won his father's kingdom back for him.

A Prince for Wales

Edward took over Wales and made his son, Edward (later Edward II), Prince of Wales. He promised the Welsh that their new prince could not speak a word of English. This was quite true - the baby prince was too young to say more than "Mama" in any language.

Eleanor Crosses

Edward adored his first wife, Eleanor of Castille. She went with him to the Crusades - very unusual in those days. According to legend, Edward was wounded and Eleanor sucked the poison out of the wound. He survived; she died. Edward put up a cross everywhere the procession carrying her coffin stopped on the way to her funeral. There were 12 altogether. The last stopping place was Charing Cross in London.

EDWARD II (HOUSE OF PLANTAGENET)

• 1284 - 1327 • crowned age 23 • king for 20 years • married Isabella of France • 1 child

Edward was a very unsuccessful king, far too fond of giving power and money to his favourites. In 1314, his army was defeated by a much smaller Scottish army led by Robert Bruce. It is said that Robert was thinking of giving up the struggle to win back Scotland from the English, when he noticed a spider spinning a web across a window. At first the spider could not leap across the gap, but it kept on trying, until at last it succeeded and spun a beautiful web. This inspired Bruce to go on and beat Edward, which he did.

Edward's favourites practically ran the country. His barons did not like this; they got together with the Queen and forced Edward to abdicate: to give up his kingdom. He was imprisoned and later murdered.

EDWARD III (HOUSE OF PLANTAGENET)

> • 1312 - 1377 • crowned age 15 • king for 50 years
> • married Philippa of Hainault • 5 children

When Edward became king, his mother and her lover, Roger Mortimer, were running the country. At 18, Edward had Mortimer put to death and sent his mother away. He later made war on the Scots and the French. Edward and his son, Edward the Black Prince, won many famous victories; but they could never have done it without the English bowmen.

The English longbow could be loaded and fired much faster than a crossbow, which the French used. The war dragged on for over 100 years, and was later called the Hundred Years' War.

The Black Death

Meanwhile in England, a terrible disease called the Black Death killed a third of the people of England. Many villages just disappeared because there was nobody left alive to work the land.

The Black Prince never became king. He died just a year before his father. The Black Prince's son, Richard II, came to the throne.

RICHARD II (HOUSE OF PLANTAGENET)

> • 1367 - 1400 • crowned age 10 • king for
> 22 years • married: **1** Anne of Bohemia
> **2** Isabella of Valois • no children

The Peasants' Revolt

Richard was only 10 when he became king and a
council of nobles, led by John of Gaunt, ran the
country. John of Gaunt was Richard's uncle, and a
son of Edward III. The council made the people pay
high taxes. Some peasants marched to London and
they burned and looted, opened the prisons and
killed the Archbishop of Canterbury.

The boy king rode to meet them and promised to
put things right. He never did, but the peasants
marched peacefully home again.

After a struggle with his nobles, Richard took over
the government. He ruled sensibly and fairly at first,
but later he had many people arrested for plotting
against him. He banished (sent away) his cousin,
Henry Bolingbroke, who later came back and
forced Richard to abdicate. Henry became Henry IV.
Richard was imprisoned in Pontefract Castle, where
he was probably murdered or left to starve.

HENRY IV (HOUSE OF LANCASTER)

> • 1367 - 1413 • crowned age 32 • king for
> 14 years • married: **1** Mary Bohun
> **2** Joan of Navarre • 6 children

Henry had robbed Richard of the throne. He knew that there were other people who had more right to be king than he had.

One account of his coronation describes three bad omens which foretold a turbulent reign. Apparently, he lost a shoe, one of his spurs fell off, and his crown blew away! Not a good start...

He had trouble from Richard's supporters, as well as problems with the Welsh, the French and the Scots. However, he faced them all bravely and he hung onto the crown and passed it on to his son.

HENRY V (HOUSE OF LANCASTER)

> • 1387 - 1422 • crowned age 26 • king for 9 years
> • married Catherine of Valois • 1 child

From the age of 14, Henry fought his father's battles against the Welsh.

Fighting for France

Henry also believed he had a claim to the French crown through his great-grandfather, Edward III. The French king did not agree, and sent Henry a box of tennis balls and a message to "Go away and play!" Henry did not go away and play. He took the port of Harfleur, then won a sensational victory at Agincourt. Once again the English bowmen out-shot the French crossbowmen.

He and the French king agreed that Henry would govern France, and would be king when the French king died. Henry married the French king's daughter, Catherine, and there was peace. Sadly, Henry died in France the following year, leaving his widow, Catherine, and their baby son, Henry VI. Catherine married a Welshman called Owen Tudor. Their grandson, Henry Tudor, became King Henry VII of England (see page 21).

HENRY VI (HOUSE OF LANCASTER)

- 1421 - 1471 • became king aged 9 months
- was king for 39 years, then again for 1 year
  (the only English king to rule twice)
- married Margaret of Anjou • no children

Henry's uncles ran the kingdom for him. Henry grew up to be a gentle, weak, saintly man who suffered from mental illness and could not keep the nobles in order.

The Two Roses

Richard Duke of York had a better claim to the throne than Henry. His badge was a white rose. The badge of Henry's own House of Lancaster was a red rose.

When Henry fell ill, Parliament asked Richard to govern the country. When Henry got better, Richard tried to stay in power. That was the beginning of the Wars of the Roses, which went on for several years. In 1461, Richard's son, Edward, was proclaimed king. Henry was imprisoned and later murdered.

EDWARD IV (HOUSE OF YORK)

> • 1442 - 1483 • crowned age 19 • king for
> 22 years • married Elizabeth Woodville • 6 children

Edward had to fight, both to become king and to stay
king. The Earl of Warwick, who had helped Edward
to become king, changed sides and helped Queen
Margaret, Henry VI's wife, to get Henry back on the
throne. A year later Edward won back the throne at
the Battle of Barnet.

Edward was tall - 1.9 metres - and handsome, but
he was cruel and ruthless and had several rivals
murdered. On his deathbed, he named his brother,
Richard of Gloucester, as Protector of the Kingdom
until his son, 13 year old King Edward V, was old
enough to rule. Richard of Gloucester promptly
imprisoned King Edward V and his brother,
Prince Richard, in the Tower of London and
seized the throne.

EDWARD V (HOUSE OF YORK)

> • 1470 - 1483 • crowned age 13 • king for
> 3 months • not married • no children

When their father died, he asked his brother Richard of Gloucester, to take care of his two sons, Edward V and Richard. Instead, Richard of Gloucester shut them up in the Tower of London, where they both died. Centuries later, the bones of two boys were found in the Tower and buried in Westminster Abbey.

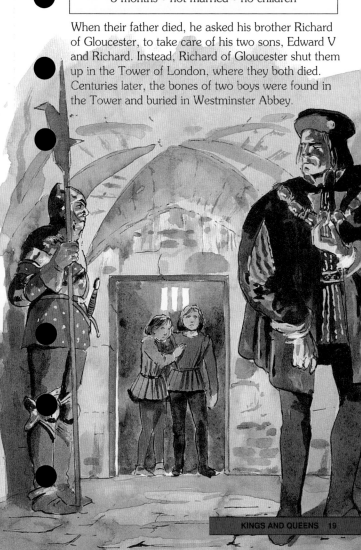

RICHARD III (HOUSE OF YORK)

> • 1452 - 1485 • crowned age 31 • king for 2 years
> • married Anne Nevill • no children

Tudor history books described Richard as ugly, cruel, deformed and a child murderer. Since then several historians have tried to prove that Richard was none of those things.

What is certain is that many people thought Richard had no right to the throne. Another claimant to the throne was Henry Tudor, who was descended from yet another son of Edward III, and the Welshman who had married Henry V's widow. Henry fought Richard - and won. Richard III was killed at the Battle of Bosworth Field; and so the House of Tudor began.

HENRY VII (HOUSE OF TUDOR)

> • 1457 - 1509 • crowned age 28 • king for
> 24 years • married Elizabeth of York • 4 children

Two Imposters

Henry had seized the crown by force and many
people wanted to remove him from the throne.
His enemies coached a baker's son, called Lambert
Simnel, and set him up as the long-lost son of
Edward IV. He ended up working in the royal
kitchens and looking after the hawks.

Perkin Warbeck claimed to be Prince Richard,
one of the little princes in the Tower. Many people
believed him and the Scottish king gave him his
daughter in marriage. He was eventually put in
prison and executed.

Henry VII asked a scholar called Polydore Vergil to
write a history of England. Vergil did so - and said
how greedy and tight-fisted Henry was. As the book
was not published until Henry was dead, Vergil got
away with it.

HENRY VIII (HOUSE OF TUDOR)

> • 1491 - 1547 • crowned age 18 • king for 38 years
> • married: **1** Catherine of Aragon **2** Anne Boleyn
>   **3** Jane Seymour **4** Anne of Cleves
> **5** Catherine Howard **6** Catherine Parr • 3 children

Henry was tall, handsome, sporty and a fine musician. Later, however, he became hugely fat and had to be hoisted onto his horse with a crane.

The Church of England

Henry, like all kings, wanted a son. He and Catherine of Aragon had just one daughter, Mary. Henry wanted to divorce Catherine and marry Anne Boleyn, who was already expecting his baby. At that time the Pope in Rome was head of the Catholic Church and Henry had to get his permission. The Pope refused, so Henry made himself head of the Church in England and married Anne anyway.

The End of the Monasteries

Henry took over all the monasteries and pocketed all their money. He gave their lands to his favourites. When people disagreed with him, he had them put to death.

HENRY VIII'S SIX WIVES

- **Catherine of Aragon.** She and Henry had one daughter, Mary.

- **Anne Boleyn.** She and Henry had a daughter, Elizabeth, but no sons. Henry decided she was unfaithful to him, and had her beheaded.

- Henry's next wife, **Jane Seymour,** died shortly after giving birth to their son Edward.

- Wife number 4 was **Anne of Cleves.** Henry called her the Flanders Mare and refused to go to bed with her. He agreed to marry her only on condition that they could be divorced straight afterwards.

- Now 50 year old Henry married 19 year old **Catherine Howard.** When she started flirting with younger men, Henry had her beheaded.

- His last wife, **Catherine Parr,** had already buried two husbands and she outlived Henry, too. She was kind to Henry's three children and protected them from his terrible rages.

- Meanwhile in Scotland, Henry VII's daughter, Margaret Tudor, had married King James IV of Scotland. This led to England and Scotland being united in 1603...

EDWARD VI (HOUSE OF TUDOR)

> • 1537 - 1553 • crowned age 10 • king for 6 years
> • not married • no children

Edward was, of course, too young to rule. The kingdom was run first by his uncle, the Duke of Somerset, then by the Duke of Northumberland. Northumberland knew Edward would not live long, and he did not want Mary, who was a Catholic, to be queen. So he persuaded Edward, on his deathbed, to name Lady Jane Grey as queen.

Lady Jane had been married against her will to Northumberland's son. She was queen for just 9 days before being imprisoned in the Tower of London, where she was beheaded, aged just 17.

MARY I (HOUSE OF TUDOR)

> • 1516 - 1558 • crowned age 37 • queen for
> 5 years • married King Philip of Spain • no children

Mary was just 12 when Henry VIII divorced her
mother and broke away from the Catholic church.
Mary herself remained a Catholic, and when she
became queen she tried to bring England back to
the old religion. She was nicknamed Bloody Mary
because of the Protestants (people who disagreed
with the Catholic faith) she burned at the stake.

Mary and Philip

Mary's husband, Philip of Spain, was 11 years
younger than she was. He was hated by the English,
who thought that after Mary's death England would
just become a part of Spain. Meanwhile England was
dragged into Spain's war with the French. England's
last bit of France - Calais - was lost. Mary was
heartbroken and said, "When I am dead you will
find Calais lying on my heart".

ELIZABETH I (HOUSE OF TUDOR)

> • 1533 - 1603 • crowned age 25 • queen for
> 45 years • not married • no children

Elizabeth, the red-haired daughter of Henry VIII and
Anne Boleyn, was a Protestant. She was a clever
woman and a successful queen, except that she had
nobody to leave the crown to after her death, except
the son of her old enemy Mary Queen of Scots.

Artists and Explorers

During Elizabeth's reign, while Shakespeare first
performed his plays in London, adventurers set out
to explore new lands. Sir Francis Drake was the first
Englishman to sail round the world.

He also led the English ships against the Spanish
Armada. To be quite honest, it was stormy weather
that defeated the Armada, but it has gone down in
history as a great English victory.

Sir Walter Raleigh, poet, explorer and a great
favourite of the Queen's, sailed to America and
brought back the first tobacco and potatoes.

MARY QUEEN OF SCOTS

Meanwhile in Scotland...

> • 1542 - 1587 • Became queen when she was
> 1 week old • queen for 25 years • married:
> **1** Francis II of France **2** Lord Darnley
> **3** Lord Bothwell

Mary was the daughter of King James V of Scotland.
She was unpopular because she was a Catholic.

Mary married Lord Darnley and they had a son,
James, in 1566. Darnley was recovering from
smallpox in Edinburgh when the whole house blew up
with him in it. Whodunnit? Probably Lord Bothwell.

He and Mary were married shortly afterwards.
The nobles hated Bothwell, Mary's army deserted
her and she fled to England. Her baby son, James,
was crowned James VI of Scotland.

Mary asked Elizabeth I of England to help her.
Elizabeth promptly locked Mary up. For 19 years
Mary was under house arrest. From time to time her
supporters plotted to set her free. At last, Elizabeth
had her beheaded; but her son, James VI of Scotland,
became James I of England after Elizabeth's death.

JAMES I (HOUSE OF STUART)

> • 1556 - 1625 • Also James VI of Scotland
> • King of Scotland aged 1 • King of England aged
> 37 • married Anne of Denmark • 3 children

James was learned, but not very sensible. He was once described as "the wisest fool in Christendom".

Gunpowder Plot

A group of English Catholics plotted to get rid of James, a Protestant. They placed barrels of gunpowder in the cellars of the Palace of Westminster and planned to blow up Parliament and the King. One of the plotters, Guy Fawkes, was caught in the cellars. He was hanged.

> **"Remember, remember the Fifth of November,**
> **Gunpowder, treason and plot.**
> **I see no reason why gunpowder treason**
> **Should ever be forgot."**

The Pilgrim Fathers

A group of Protestants, called the Puritans, were unhappy in England and thought they could have a better life in America. They sailed to America in 1620 in a small ship called the Mayflower and founded a new colony.

CHARLES I (HOUSE OF STUART)

> • 1600 - 1649 • crowned age 25 • king for
> 24 years • married Henrietta Maria of France
> • 7 children

Charles was a sickly child, who did not talk until
he was almost 5 and crawled until he was 7. He
outgrew his disabilities, except for a stammer,
and became a fine horseman as well as a scholar.

Charles and Parliament

Charles believed in the Divine Right of Kings - he
thought God had made him king, and that he could
rule the country as he wished. This led to him being
beheaded as a "tyrant, traitor and murderer".

He faced the headsman on a snowy day. He insisted
on wearing two shirts in case he shivered with cold
and the people thought he was shivering with fear.

Cavaliers and Roundheads

Charles's supporters were called the Cavaliers.
His enemies were called the Roundheads because of
their short haircuts. After Charles was beheaded the
country was ruled by the leader of the Roundheads,
Oliver Cromwell...

THE COMMONWEALTH

From 1649 to 1660, England was ruled by the Commonwealth (which in those days meant 'the good of everyone'). They abolished kings, the House of Lords and the Church of England. Cromwell was offered the crown of England but he said sternly, "Take away that bauble". This story is often quoted to show how sensible he was. In fact, if he had accepted the crown he would have set limits on his powers. As it was, his power was total.

After Cromwell died in 1658, the Commonwealth crumbled and in 1660, Charles Stuart was asked to come back and become Charles II.

Cromwell's Vandals

Roundheads were Puritans, who were against beautiful statues, stained glass and carvings. Instead of letting other people do what suited them, they sent people round to smash what they called "superstitious images" in churches. They even made the local people pay for this. When you see a statue with the head and hands chopped off, you can be sure the Roundheads did it.

CHARLES II (HOUSE OF STUART)

> • 1630 - 1685 • crowned age 30 • king for
> 25 years • married Catherine of Braganza
> • 13 children outside marriage

The Royal Oak

Charles escaped to France during the Civil War.
When the Roundheads were hunting for him he
hid in an oak tree. There are many pubs called the
Royal Oak in honour of the one that saved his life.

The Plague and the Fire

In 1665, during Charles's reign, the Great Plague
broke out. It was caused by fleas on rats in London's
filthy streets. Thousands of people died horribly and
their bodies were dragged away in carts and thrown
into huge pits.

In 1666, a fire broke out in London. Huge areas
of the city were destroyed. Fortunately, fire
destroyed many of the places where the plague
germs were worst.

Charles was nicknamed the Merry Monarch because
of his lifestyle. He was so fond of horseracing that he
moved his court to Newmarket during the racing
season. Although he and his mistresses had 13
children, he and the Queen were childless and the
throne passed to his brother, James.

JAMES II (HOUSE OF STUART)

> • 1633 - 1701 • crowned age 52 • king for
> 3 years • married: **1** Anne Hyde
> **2** Mary of Modena • 3 children

James was Charles II's brother. He became a
Catholic when he married his Italian wife. He wanted
to make England Catholic, but the people and
Parliament objected strongly.

Monmouth's Rebellion

The Duke of Monmouth, who was the son of
Charles II and his mistress, Lucy Walter, tried to seize
the crown. He was beheaded. James appointed
Judge Jeffreys to try Monmouth's followers. His
court was called the Bloody Assize.

James was so unpopular that Parliament invited his
nephew, William of Orange, and his wife Mary, who
was James's daughter, to become king and queen.
James escaped to France. Judge Jeffreys tried to do
the same, but was caught and sent to the Tower of
London, where he was put to death.

> • William 1650 - 1702 • Mary 1662 - 1694
> • crowned in 1689 • king for 13 years
> (queen for 5) • no children

Mary and William came over from Orange (in what is now Holland). Their arrival was called "The Glorious Revolution" because James II had been got rid of without any bloodshed.

Rebellions

However, James II landed in Ireland to try and get his kingdom back. The bloody rebellion ended with William defeating James in the Battle of the Boyne.

Meanwhile in Scotland, "Bonnie" Dundee (a Viscount) led an army in support of James. He was killed at the Battle of Killiecrankie.

The Gentleman in Black Velvet

William died when his horse stumbled over a molehill, and Mary's sister, Anne, became queen. In Scotland the Jacobites - people who wanted James II back (Jacobus is Latin for James) - used to drink toasts to the mole which killed William, saying "Here's to the little gentleman in the black velvet coat!"

ANNE (HOUSE OF STUART)

> • 1665 - 1714 • crowned age 37 • queen for
> 12 years • married Prince George of Denmark
> • 17 children

During Anne's reign England and Scotland became
united with one Parliament. Her great general, the
Duke of Marlborough, won many victories against
the French. But in the end she sent him away and
quarrelled with his wife, who was her dearest friend.

Anne herself was a sad lady. She was very fat, very
short-sighted and very lame, and all her 17 children
died young. When she died, George, who was
descended from James I's daughter Elizabeth,
became king.

GEORGE I (HOUSE OF HANOVER)

• 1660 - 1727 • crowned age 54 • king for 13 years • married Sophia Dorothea of Zell • 1 child

George was Elector of Hanover. He preferred to stay there and let a Prime Minister look after Britain. He spoke hardly any English. He divorced his wife for having an affair with a Swedish nobleman, locked her safely away and lived openly with two mistresses, one very fat, the other very thin.

More Jacobites

In Scotland the Jacobites were causing trouble again. They supported James II's son, James Edward Stuart, and invaded England to try to put him on the throne. James came from France, caught a dreadful cold and went home again.

GEORGE II (HOUSE OF HANOVER)

• 1683 - 1760 • crowned age 44 • king for 33 years • married Caroline of Anspach • 7 children

George spoke English but, like his father, preferred to spend as much time as possible in Germany and he and his queen were never popular in Britain. During his reign, Canada and India became part of the British Empire. Britain also got involved in Hanover's wars: George was the last British king to lead an army into battle.

Still More Jacobites

James Edward Stuart had a son, Charles Edward, "Bonnie Prince Charlie", who landed in Scotland in 1745 and raised an army of loyal Jacobites. They were defeated at Culloden.

Bagpipes and Highland dress were banned and many Scots were shipped abroad. Meanwhile there was a £30,000 reward for Bonnie Prince Charlie, but nobody betrayed him. A Scots girl, Flora Macdonald, dressed him as her maid and helped him to escape. He spent the rest of his life in Europe, calling himself Charles III.

GEORGE III (HOUSE OF HANOVER)

> • 1738 - 1820 • crowned age 22 • king for
> 60 years • married Charlotte of Mecklenburg
> • 15 children

George was George II's grandson. During his reign many important things happened:

Britain lost her lands in America. George Washington defeated the British Army in the American War of Independence and became the first President of the United States of America.

The French Revolution broke out. Many French nobles were beheaded by Mr Guillotin's infamous invention. Soon Britain and France were at war. The French general, Napoleon Bonaparte, created himself Emperor and ruled most of Europe.

The British Navy ruled the waves. Lord Nelson defeated the French Navy at the Battle of Trafalgar. The Duke of Wellington defeated Napoleon at the Battle of Waterloo. Wellington lived on for many years and became Prime Minister of Britain.

King George suffered from a disease called porphyria, which made him both blind and mad. For many years his son, George, ruled the kingdom as Prince Regent.

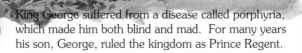

GEORGE IV (HOUSE OF HANOVER)

• 1762 - 1830 • crowned age 58 • king for
10 years • married Caroline of Brunswick
• no children

The time when George ruled Britain for his sick
father was called the Regency. It was a time of
great fashion and elegance. George built himself
an amazing Indian style palace, the Royal Pavilion
in Brighton.

George himself had many mistresses and an
extravagant lifestyle - he only agreed to marry
Princess Caroline when Parliament agreed to pay
his debts of £650,000. Later he tried to divorce her,
and he even banned her from Westminster Abbey
at his coronation. He gave great support to the arts.

WILLIAM IV (HOUSE OF HANOVER)

- 1765 - 1837 • crowned age 65 • king for 7 years
  - married Princess Adelaide of Saxe-Meinigen
  - 10 children outside marriage

William was often called the Sailor King. He joined the Navy when he was 14. He never expected to be king. He lived happily for 21 years with an actress, Dorothy Jordan. They had 10 children.

Eventually he realised that George IV would not have any children and that it was his duty to marry. He ditched poor Dorothy and married Adelaide. Their two daughters died very young, and William realised that his niece, Victoria, would be next in line to the throne. He was old and sick, but he was determined to stay alive until Victoria was old enough to rule by herself. He just made it; she was 18 when he died.

VICTORIA (HOUSE OF HANOVER)

> • 1819 - 1901 • crowned age 18 • queen for
> 64 years • married Prince Albert of Saxe-Coburg
> • 9 children

Victoria was a very good queen, who took her job most seriously. Her husband, Prince Albert, was even more serious-minded than she was. They were a devoted couple and had 9 children.

New Things

Many exciting things happened during Victoria's reign. She was the first monarch to be photographed, and to travel by train.

After Prince Albert died, Victoria hid herself away, which made her unpopular. Then the Prime Minister, Disraeli, had her created Empress of India and persuaded her to appear in public again.

Victoria has gone down in history as saying "We are not amused". In her diaries, however, she often wrote, "I was much amused". Although she took her duties seriously, she had a great sense of fun.

• 1841 - 1910 • crowned age 60 • king for
9 years • married Princess Alexandra of Denmark
• 5 children

Victoria did not much like Edward, and never gave
him anything useful to do. He spent his long, long
time as Prince of Wales shooting, gambling and
having a succession of mistresses.

However, he was the first royal prince to visit the
USA and Canada, and his visits to France improved
Anglo-French relations. Once he became king,
Edward took his duties very seriously and became
popular with the people. His reign saw many social
and intellectual advances. Old age pensions were
first given in Edwardian times.

GEORGE V (HOUSE OF WINDSOR)

> • 1865 - 1936 • crowned age 45 • king for
> 26 years • married Princess May (Mary) of Teck
> • 5 children

George was Edward VII's second son. He never
expected to be king and went into the Navy. But
his elder brother, Prince Eddy, died and George
inherited both the crown and Eddy's bride.

War!

During George's reign the First World War broke
out with Germany. George decided to change the
royal name from the German Saxe-Coburg to
Windsor, after Windsor Castle.

In the News

Thanks to cinema and photographs in newspapers
and magazines, ordinary people saw much more
of the royal family. George was seen opening great
buildings and visiting soldiers on the battlefield.
He was also the first monarch to give a Christmas
radio message.

EDWARD VIII (HOUSE OF WINDSOR)

> • 1894 - 1972 • became king when he was 42
> • king for less than 1 year (never crowned)
> • married Wallis Simpson • no children

Edward was George V's eldest son. He was a great success as Prince of Wales. He was in both the Navy and the Army, fought in World War I and did a lot of travelling on royal business. In January 1936, he became king, but he was determined to marry an American lady, Mrs Wallis Simpson, who had already been divorced twice.

He had to choose between being king without Wallis, or abdicating and marrying her. He decided to abdicate, and in December 1936, he made a moving speech explaining his reasons. He became Duke of Windsor and he and his wife went to live abroad. His younger brother became George VI.

> • 1895 - 1952 • crowned age 41 • king for
> 16 years • married Lady Elizabeth Bowes-Lyon
> • 2 children

George served both in the Navy and the Air Force.
He also became a fine tennis player and competed
at Wimbledon.

He was a shy man with a stutter. Official duties were
difficult for him, especially his Christmas broadcast,
but he took his job seriously and people liked and
respected him for it.

A Royal Family

During World War II, when the enemy bombed
London and other big cities and many people moved
out of town, the royal family stayed in London and
kept everyone's spirits up with visits to bomb sites
and hospitals.

The young princesses did war work, too - Princess
Elizabeth became a motor mechanic. And when
everything was rationed, from meat to petrol, the
royal family went short, too. Can you imagine
Henry VIII rationing himself to 100 grams of meat
a week?

ELIZABETH II (HOUSE OF WINDSOR)

> • Born 1926 • crowned age 26 • married Prince
> Philip, Duke of Edinburgh • 4 children

Queen Elizabeth II has already ruled for over
40 years. She is the most travelled monarch ever.
She has been all round the world several times.

There have been many changes in her lifetime.
There is no longer a British Empire, but she is head
of a huge Commonwealth. She takes her work
seriously and is very good at it; but she enjoys
the outdoor life. The royal family are forever in the
public eye, and are a popular selling-point for the
country's tourist trade and the tabloid newspapers!

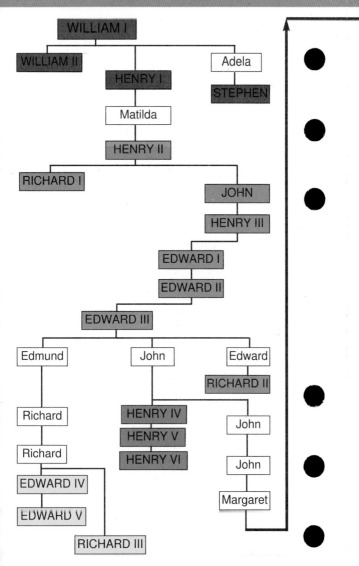

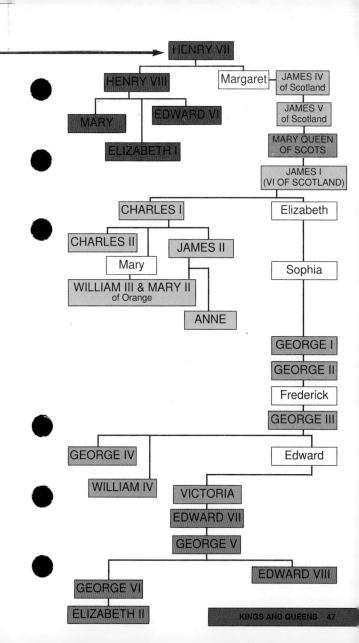

HENRY VII

HENRY VIII — Margaret — JAMES IV of Scotland

MARY   EDWARD VI

ELIZABETH I

JAMES V of Scotland

MARY QUEEN OF SCOTS

JAMES I (VI OF SCOTLAND)

CHARLES I   Elizabeth

CHARLES II   JAMES II

Mary

WILLIAM III & MARY II of Orange

ANNE

Sophia

GEORGE I

GEORGE II

Frederick

GEORGE III

GEORGE IV   Edward

WILLIAM IV

VICTORIA

EDWARD VII

GEORGE V

EDWARD VIII

GEORGE VI

ELIZABETH II

USELESS INFORMATION!

William I became very fat and his body was too big for its stone coffin. When the attendants were trying to cram it in, the body burst, filling the church with a disgusting smell.

Richard I composed several songs in Old French. When Richard was taken prisoner a minstrel, Blondin, found him by wandering from castle to castle, singing Richard's songs. At last, the royal voice joined in the chorus: the minstrel had found his master.

King John is famous for losing his belongings in the Wash - not a laundry, but the big bay on the east coast of England. His baggage train got bogged down, the tide came in and all John's valuables were lost.

Henry III kept a zoo in the Tower of London.

Henry IV was told he would die in Jerusalem. He thought this meant on a Crusade; but in fact he died in the Jerusalem Chamber at the Palace of Wesminster.

James I described smoking as "loathsome to the eye, hateful to the nose, harmful to the brain and dangerous to the lungs".

Queen Anne suffered terribly from gout. To ease the pain she drank brandy out of a teacup, asking for "More cold tea, please".

George IV wore make-up and corsets.

Edward VII loved practical jokes. One of his favourites was to put a dead rabbit in someone's bed.

Page 4

Page 29

Page 8

Page 21

Page 12

Page 8

Page 13

Page 35

Page 37

Page 9

Page 28

Page 31

Page 7

Page 26

Page 17

Page 23

Page 39

Page 45

Page 15

Page 7

Page 6

Page 19